Saint Demiana

and Her Forty Friends

Edited by
Yostina Youssef

Illustrated by
Mina Anton

Coloring Book for Children

Saint Demiana
and Her Forty Friends
Coloring Book for Children

© 2019 by ACTS Press

AC✠S
P·R·E·S·S

www.acts.press

ISBN 978-1-940661-13-1

Printed in the United States of America

A Word from the Editor

'Therefore, children, let us hold fast to the practice of asceticism and not grow careless. For, in this, we have the Lord working with us, as it is written: "To all that choose the good, the Lord works with them for good" (Ro 8:28).[1]

With great joy, we present to our beloved parents and children alike this Coptic Orthodox coloring book for children published by ACTS Press under the auspices of His Eminence Metropolitan Serapion and the guidance of His Grace Bishop Kyrillos, Auxiliary Bishop for Christian Education in the Diocese of Los Angeles, Southern California, and Hawaii.

The goal of Orthodox Christianity is to unite every aspect of person's life with Christ. Nowhere is this more evident than with our children. We baptize them shortly after birth and immediately unite them with Christ through the life of the Church and participation in the Holy Mysteries. We feed their minds with the inspired words of Holy Scripture and teach them to sanctify their bodies through fasting and purity. Throughout this lifelong journey to holiness, we also connect them with the choirs of the holy saints, the heroes of the Church, as friends and role models for life.

This coloring book is presented as a wholesome activity to help parents and children develop a relationship with Saint Demiana and the Forty Virgins, whose life and martyrdom are a beacon of light for every faithful Christian. This text was originally prepared by the blessed nuns of St. Demiana Coptic Orthodox Convent near Damietta, Egypt, and adapted by Yostina Youssef. With simple language and engaging illustrations, children are encouraged to meditate on their life and internalize their virtues, which ultimately will lead them closer to Christ Himself. Not only will children benefit, but also parents who complete this beautiful activity with their children, for parents are the first models of holiness for their children. When children see their parents reflecting the love, patience, and holiness of the saints, they necessarily imitate them.

For this reason, we encourage parents and children alike to dedicate some time to the study of Saint Demiana and color these pages with faith and love as they both grow in their relationship with God and with one another.

The Editor

---

1   St. Athanasius, *"Life of St. Anthony,"* in *Early Christian Biographies*, ed. Hermigild Dressler and Roy J. Deferrari, trans. Mary Emily Keenan, vol. 15, The Fathers of the Church (Washington, DC: The Catholic University of America Press, 1952), 152.

Ϧⲉⲛ ⲫⲣⲁⲛ ⲙ̀Ⲫⲓⲱⲧ ⲛⲉⲙ Ⲡϣⲏⲣⲓ ⲛⲉⲙ Ⲡⲓⲡ̀ⲛⲉⲩⲙⲁ ⲉⲑⲟⲩⲁⲃ.

Ⲟⲩⲛⲟⲩϯ ⲛ̀ⲟⲩⲱⲧ. Ⲁⲙⲏⲛ.

In the Name of the Father, the Son, and the Holy Spirit.

One God. Amen.

Near the end

of the third century, there lived a Christian man named Mark. He was the governor of El-Borollos and El-Zaafaran districts on the northern delta of the Nile River in Egypt. Mark had an only child named Demiana. She was famous for her beauty and holiness. Her father loved her dearly.

St. Demiana's mother went to heaven when she was a young girl, so her father raised her alone. St. Demiana grew up loving to pray and reading the Bible.

When St. Demiana became older, her father wanted her to marry one of his noble friends; however, she did not want to marry. She wanted to be a bride of Christ so she could serve her Lord and Savior for the rest of her life.

St. Demiana asked

her father to build her a house near the edge of the city where she could live with her friends, praying and working for God, alone. Knowing her deep desire for a holy life, her father granted her wish and built her a large palace in the wilderness.

St. Demiana turned the palace into a Coptic Orthodox monastery for nuns. The Lord's hand was with them, giving them strength and comfort. With St. Demiana as their spiritual mother, they spent their time fasting, doing handiwork, reading the holy books, and praying to God.

At that time, the Roman Emperor Diocletian began to treat Christians very badly. When Mark, St. Demiana's father, was ordered to kneel before the idols and offer incense, he refused at first. After some time, he put God behind him and worshiped the idols.

When St. Demiana

found out that her father had denied Christ, she quickly left her palace and went to see her father. When she saw him, she said, "What have I heard about you? I wish I had heard the news of your death rather than knowing you have left God, Who created you. What you did, my father, is wrong. If you keep on worshipping idols, then you are not my father. It is better for you to die as a martyr and live with Christ in heaven forever than to live as an unbeliever here."

Her father was moved by her words and cried with repentance. He confessed and said, "I am a sinner. God forgive me!" Mark went right away to Antioch to see Emperor Diocletian. Mark said to Emperor Diocletian, "How could you leave the worship of the God of heaven and earth and worship idols made by rocks and wood, who are deaf and mute?"

Mark then made

the sign of the cross and shouted, "I believe in the Father, Son and Holy Spirit; One God, Amen." St. Mark earned the crown of martyrdom and was rewarded with a life with Christ in heaven. The feast day of his martyrdom is commemorated on July 12 (Abib 5 in the Coptic calendar).

When Emperor Diocletian

learned that it was St. Demiana who had convinced her
father to return to worship our Lord Jesus Christ, he
ordered one of his commanders to attack her palace.
Diocletian said, "First, try to convince her to worship
our idols by offering her treasure. But if she refuses,
then hurt and even kill her and her friends so all
Christians learn to leave Christ."

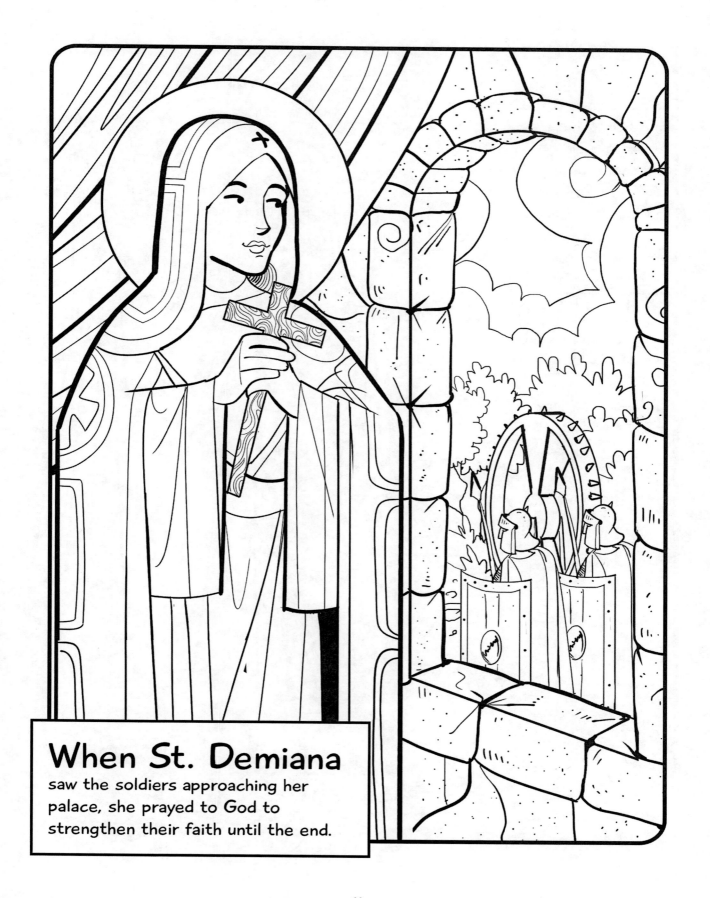

When St. Demiana

saw the soldiers approaching her palace, she prayed to God to strengthen their faith until the end.

The bad commander and soldiers hurt the holy saints many times, but every time, St. Demiana reminded her friends what St. Paul said in the Bible: "For I consider that the sufferings of this present time are not worthy to be compared with the glory which shall be revealed in us" (Ro 8:18).

Each time, Archangel Michael appeared, lit up their prison with glorious light, gave them peace, and healed them completely.

In the morning, the prince ordered St. Demiana to be brought to the court. When he saw that St. Demiana had been healed without a single scratch on her body, he could not believe it! The crowd screamed, saying, "O unfair prince, we declare we are all Christians and we believe in the Lord Jesus Christ, the God of this saint, St. Demiana." About four hundred people earned the crowns of martyrdom and became intercessors for their village.

After hurting the holy saints for a long time, God healed them each time. Finally, St. Demiana and her 40 holy friends entered the Heavenly Kingdom with their beloved Christ and earned the crown of martyrdom. We celebrate their victory on January 21 (Tubah 13 in the Coptic calendar), May the prayers and blessings of these great martyr saints, Saint Demiana and the 40 virgins, be with us all, Amen.